TOILETING ISSUES

Kathryn Fenton
with Ellie Johnson

Published by
CoramBAAF Adoption and Fostering Academy
41 Brunswick Square
London WC1N 1AZ
www.corambaaf.org.uk

Coram Academy Limited, registered as a company limited by
guarantee in England and Wales number 9697712, part of the
Coram group, charity number 312278

British Library Cataloguing in Publication Data
A catalogue record for this book is available from the British Library

ISBN 978 1 910039 80 9

Project management by Jo Francis, Publications, CoramBAAF
Designed and typeset by Fravashi Aga
Printed in Great Britain by the Lavenham Press
Trade distribution by Turnaround Publisher Services, Unit 3,
Olympia Trading Estate, Coburg Road, London N22 6TZ

Contents

Notes about the authors

Kathryn Fenton is a Child and Adolescent Psychotherapist at the Tavistock and Portman NHS Foundation Trust. Trained as a social worker, she has a strong interest in applied psychoanalytic work in a variety of settings. She was a member of the Tavistock Fostering, Adoption and Kinship Care Team and worked for many years as an expert witness in the family courts, as well as offering treatment interventions to children and young people who have been fostered and adopted.

Ellie Johnson joined the team at CoramBAAF in 2017 as the Health Consultant. For 14 years previously, she was a LAC (looked after children) nurse. She was based in a multi-agency team and worked with many adopted and fostered children and young people, foster carers and adopters.

The series editor

Hedi Argent is an established author/editor for CoramBAAF. Her books cover a wide range of family placement topics and she has written several guides and a story book for young children.

Acknowledgements

My thanks to the children, young people and families who have shared their experiences with me, from whom I have learned so much, and without whom this book would not have been written.
Kathryn Fenton

The contribution I have made to this book comes from working with, and learning from, so many wonderful adopted and fostered children and their families.
Ellie Johnson

We are grateful to Phillida Sawbridge and Biddy Youell for reading an earlier draft and for their helpful comments.

Looking behind the label…

Jack has mild learning difficulties and displays some characteristics of ADHD and it is uncertain whether this will increase…

Beth and Mary both have a diagnosis of global developmental delay…

Abigail's birth mother has a history of substance abuse. There is no clear evidence that Abigail was prenatally exposed to drugs but her new family will have to accept developmental uncertainty…

Jade has some literacy and numeracy difficulties, but has made some improvement with the support of a learning mentor…

Prospective adopters and carers are often faced with the prospect of having to decide whether they can care for a child with a health need or condition they know little about and have no direct experience of. No easy task…

Will Jack's learning difficulties become more severe?
Will Beth and Mary be able to catch up?
When will it be clear whether or not Abigail has been affected by parental substance misuse?
And will Jade need a learning mentor throughout her school life?

It can be difficult to know where to turn for reliable information. What lies behind the diagnoses and "labels" that many looked after children bring with them? And what will it be like to live with them? How will they benefit from family life?

Parenting Matters is a unique series, "inspired" by the terms used – and the need to "decode" them – in profiles of children needing new permanent families. Each title provides expert knowledge about a particular condition, coupled with facts, figures and guidance presented in a straightforward and accessible style. Each book also describes what it is like to parent an affected child, with either case studies or adopters and foster carers "telling it like it is", sharing their parenting experiences, and offering useful advice. This combination of expert information and first-hand experiences will help readers to gain understanding, and to make informed decisions.

Titles in the series deal with a wide range of health conditions and steer readers to where they can find more information. They offer a sound introduction to the topic under consideration and provide a glimpse of what it would be like to live with an affected child. Most importantly, this series looks behind the label and gives families the confidence to look more closely at a child whom they otherwise might have passed by.

Keep up with all our new books as they are published by signing up to our free publications bulletin at: https://corambaaf.org.uk/subscribe.

Shaila Shah, Publications Department, CoramBAAF

Titles in this series include:

- *Parenting a Child with Attention Deficit Hyperactivity Disorder*
- *Parenting a Child with Dyslexia*
- *Parenting a Child with Mental Health Issues*
- *Parenting a Child affected by Parental Substance Misuse*
- *Parenting a Child with Emotional and Behavioural Difficulties*
- *Parenting a Child with Autism Spectrum Disorder*
- *Parenting a Child with Developmental Delay*
- *Parenting a Child with, or at risk of, Genetic Disorders*
- *Parenting a Child affected by Domestic Violence*
- *Parenting a Child affected by Sexual Abuse*
- *Parenting a Child who has experienced Trauma*

Introduction

Wetting and soiling by children is not a new problem – it is something that occurs quite frequently in the general population. There is plenty of very comprehensive practical information and support available to help parents and carers when the problem arises. However, this tends to focus primarily on the *physical* causes of wetting and soiling and how best to manage them in a practical way.

Of course, the physical causes of the problem should be investigated in the first instance. Indeed, whatever the cause, it will have to be managed in a practical as well as a sensitive way. I will therefore be exploring some of the physical causes of wetting and soiling as well as making reference to resources that are widely available to help parents and carers. But the focus of this book will be on the issue of *wetting and soiling when it relates specifically to looked after and adopted children*. My intention is to examine some of the possible underlying emotional and/or psychological causes, and to consider how toileting issues can sometimes be understood as a way for children to communicate their difficulties. I hope to support foster carers' and adoptive parents' *own understanding* of the issue and the possible meaning of the communication/behaviour.

I am mindful that children who have been in the care system will have had contact with many professionals, and will arrive in foster care placements or move to adoptive families accompanied by reports that can feel hard for carers or parents to digest and comprehend. I have provided some helpful definitions below and a glossary of terms at the end of this book in case some of the terms and phrases I have used are unfamiliar to the reader. I introduce these terms in bold type for ease of cross referencing. When talking to children about their toilet habits, it is important to use language that they themselves use or are able to understand and feel comfortable with. Therefore, I sometimes use the term "wee" when referring to urine and "poo" when referring to faeces.

I refer to the child as "he" throughout the book and to carers as "she", in order to avoid confusion.

Useful definitions

Terminology	Meaning
Diurnal enuresis (daytime wetting)	This term refers to when a child who is toilet trained has wetting accidents during the day. This can be anything from damp patches in their pants to a full-blown "accident". Some children who have daytime wetting also wet the bed.
Nocturnal enuresis (bedwetting)	This term refers to the unintentional passing of urine during sleep.

Encopresis (soiling)	This term refers to the soiling of underwear by children who are past the age of toilet training. It occurs when a child dirties his pants or poos in inappropriate places, for example, on his bed, or in rooms other than the toilet.
Scatolia (smearing)	This term refers to playing with and/or smearing of poo.
Continence	This term refers to bowel and bladder control.

Who is this book for?

This book has been written with the aim of creating a deeper understanding of the potential emotional and psychological causes of wetting and soiling by children and young people who have been adopted or are in the care of the local authority. It will be of help to adoptive parents, prospective adopters, foster carers, social workers, looked after children (LAC) nurses, school nurses, residential staff, teachers, and other professionals involved in supporting children who are in foster or adoptive homes.

SECTION 1

UNDERSTANDING TOILETING ISSUES

KATHRYN FENTON

CHAPTER 1

The challenges of parenting looked after and adopted children

Caring for children who have been removed from their birth families can be very rewarding and satisfying, but it can also be an extremely difficult and demanding task. A child who is wetting, soiling or smearing, or indeed doing all three, may add a layer of frustration to what can already feel like an overwhelming responsibility. This highly sensitive and often taboo subject can then become the tipping point for adoptive parents and foster carers doing their very best for children who face challenges in many other aspects of their lives.

It can feel highly provocative when a child seems to be deliberately wetting or soiling. Managing the problem can feel like an impossible task at times, and can cause tension, frustration and even anger when carers feel helpless about how to manage the situation. It is a problem that can feel embarrassing to talk about; it is distressing for all concerned; and it can have a significant impact on a child's or young person's sense of dignity and self-esteem, as well as being a potential cause of placement breakdown. Parents, carers and professionals often feel under a great deal of pressure to resolve the problem quickly before a child moves to a different placement or starts nursery or school, which leaves everyone concerned in a heightened state of anxiety that may only serve to exacerbate the issue. Unfortunately, there is rarely a quick solution of the difficulty, which can be quite deeply rooted and is often linked to the child's early experiences.

Theoretical perspectives

I will begin by considering some of the challenges that children in the care system face as a result of their early experiences.

On 31 March 2018, there were 75,420 children in the care of local authorities in England, of whom 53,200 were in foster care placements (Department for Education, 2018). There is extensive evidence from **attachment** theory, developments in **neuroscience** and child development research to highlight the link between adverse childhood experiences and long-term negative outcomes (Schore, 2001; Meltzer et al, 2003). Children who have been removed from their birth families and taken into local authority care are amongst the most vulnerable and disadvantaged groups in our society. They may have been subject to neglect, emotional, physical or sexual abuse, or indeed all four. They may have been exposed to domestic violence, parental mental illness or substance abuse. This list is not exhaustive, but it describes some of the experiences that would be considered as having a long-lasting, adverse impact on children's overall development. These children will undoubtedly have been traumatised by their experiences, whatever their age when they entered the care system.

It is not uncommon for carers and professionals to assume that

4

because a child was removed into care immediately after birth, or adopted as a baby, his early experiences will have had a minimal impact. This is not at all to say that foster carers, professionals or adoptive parents are not in touch with the painful reality of children's losses and experiences, but rather that there is a deep-seated hope that the child will not remember them. 'They were too young to remember', or 'They didn't see anything', are comments that I have heard many times in my work with foster carers and adoptive parents as they struggle to understand some of the behaviour they are having to manage.

However, developments in neuroscience and technology have helped us to understand that babies' brains are shaped by their earliest experiences. Research shows that there are links between a baby's **physiological** development and the mother's hormonal state, and that various physical and emotional factors in the mother's life can have an impact on the nature and quality of the **intra-uterine** experience of the developing foetus. It has long been acknowledged that the use of alcohol and drugs in pregnancy has an adverse effect on the developing foetus, but more recent research has also shown that **cortisol**, the maternally produced stress hormone, passes through the placental wall into the baby's bloodstream. Studies have highlighted correlations between maternal and foetal cortisol levels.

Attachment theory shows that babies need sensitive and attuned parenting in order to support and facilitate their healthy emotional and psychological development. The type of attachments children form, and to a large degree the quality of their future relationships, are strongly dependent on the quality of the experience they have had with their primary caregivers.

John Bowlby, a psychiatrist and psychoanalyst best known for his development of attachment theory, concluded that: 'The infant and young child should experience a warm, intimate and continuous

SECTION I

5

relationship with his mother (or permanent substitute) in which both find satisfaction and enjoyment' (Bowlby, 1951).

Related to this, and of central importance, is the psychoanalyst Wilfred Bion's concept of the mother being a "container" for her baby's emotions. Bion recognised that the baby's **psyche**/mind is not strong enough to contain the powerful feelings that threaten to completely overwhelm him at times of distress. He describes how the infant needs an attentive carer who can take in and think about his feelings of distress without becoming overwhelmed by them herself. When a mother can make sense of her baby's communications in her own mind, she is able to tend to his needs in a way that helps to make him feel safe. As a result, the baby experiences his feelings and his sense of "physically falling apart" being gathered up and "contained" (Bion, 1962).

In time, through repeatedly having a thoughtful and attentive parent available to tolerate and make sense of his feelings, the infant is able to begin to regulate himself. This is not to say that all babies do not experience periods of distress, but to illustrate how from a very early stage, if the parenting is "'good enough" and infants are actively supported in a psychological and emotional way by being held in mind by their mother or primary caregiver, they can begin to manage their own emotions.

Sadly, many children who have come into the care system have not had this experience and have too often been left to manage on their own. In these cases, they may find alternative ways of managing emotional upset, which can have an adverse impact on their emotional and psychological development. I will explore this in more detail later in the book.

As a result of adverse early experiences, children who have been fostered or adopted have needs that are over and above those of other children of their age. Their capacity to move on to more healthy trajectories after an adverse start in life is dependent on many factors. These can include, for example, whether there have been other helpful, available adults, who can be regarded as "**protective factors**", and who may have supported the child to develop some level of resilience in spite of the context in which they were living. Much will depend on the nature and quality of care that they received in subsequent placements.

I have drawn attention to these concepts because they are fundamental to the development of the healthy emotional apparatus of the child, and I will return to them at various points to illustrate factors related to wetting, soiling and toileting difficulties.

Specific issues around trauma and sexual abuse have been explored in other books in this series; I will consider how they might specifically relate to toileting problems when children and young people are placed in foster care or have been adopted.

SECTION I

CHAPTER **2**

Bedwetting and soiling: a common problem?

Wetting and soiling is not unusual during early infancy and childhood. Children develop at different rates, but in general most parents begin toilet training their children between the ages of around two and two-and-a-half years. By the age of three children are dry most days, but even then, they have the odd accident, especially when they are excited, upset or absorbed in something else. By the age of four, most children are dry during the day. Becoming dry at night is a developmental skill, and like other developmental milestones, children will achieve it at different times. Although most have mastered it between the ages of three and five, up to one in five children aged five sometimes wets the bed.

According to **NICE** (National Institute for Clinical Excellence, 2010a), **nocturnal enuresis** (defined as bedwetting more than two nights each week) has a prevalence of eight per cent for children of four-and-a-half years, reducing to 1.9 per cent at nine years and seven months.

Around 900,000 children and young people in the UK have continence problems (NHS England). A study undertaken by the University of Bristol (Joinson, 2018) highlighted the following incidence in the general teenage population:

- urinary incontinence is most common (3–4% of teenagers);

- bedwetting (2–3% of teenagers);

- soiling (1–2% of teenagers).

An earlier study of healthy adolescents indicated that three per cent of 15–16-year-olds experienced regular daytime wetting, and nocturnal enuresis was reported in 1.1 per cent of the same age group (Weaver et al, 2004).

Therefore, it is not uncommon for children and young people within the general population to experience problems of wetting and soiling. Whatever their background, these difficulties can take a long time to resolve, will require careful and sensitive management, and will have a profound impact on a young person's quality of life, self-confidence and self-esteem.

The prevalence of wetting and soiling in looked after children

Statistics have highlighted that wetting and soiling problems affect looked after children more often than children living with their own families, and bedwetting in particular has been found to be more prevalent in children who are in the care of local authorities (Williams et al, 2001). It was also one of the most commonly reported physical complaints in a national survey of children and

9

young people, aged between 5–17 years and looked after by local authorities in England (Meltzer *et al*, 2003; see also Gould, 2011).

The study undertaken by Meltzer *et al* showed that a substantial number of looked after children aged five or over wet the bed (17.9%), and for children in the 11–15 age group, 15.2 per cent still wet the bed, whereas only five per cent of young people in the general population wet the bed.

A study of the case files of 648 children across six local authorities, at the point of their entry into care, found that the children aged five years and over who wet the bed were all reported to have signs of emotional and behavioural problems compared with those who did not wet the bed. In the 11–15-year-old age group, children who wet the bed were more likely to have entered care as a result of abuse or neglect compared with those who did not wet the bed (Sempik *et al*, 2008).

The prevalence of bedwetting (17%) reported in Sempik and colleagues' study was similar to that of 16 per cent found previously by Meltzer *et al* (2003) in their study of looked after children. Sempik *et al* suggest therefore that these findings represent a reliable assessment of the extent of the problem and its **aetiology**.

Other studies have reported that bedwetting is associated with becoming looked after, especially in older children who have experienced a high incidence of parental separation, parental disharmony, and early moves from home (Butler, 1994; Jarvelin *et al*, 1990; Kalo and Bella, 1996; von Gontard *et al*, 1997).

The high prevalence of nocturnal enuresis makes it important to consider the specific issues it may raise for looked after children and young people. For example, it has been found that bedwetting may cause children to feel perplexed, humiliated and socially isolated; they are usually afraid of detection and often immature (Anon, 1987; Butler, 1987, 1994).

All these findings underline the importance of professional, comprehensive assessments of children's and young people's emotional and behavioural development, as well as their physical developmental needs, prior to their placement with foster carers or move to potential adoptive families. Children presenting with complex needs will often require long-term, specialist support. Therefore, it is important that foster carers and potential adopters are adequately prepared for probable and possible difficulties. They require access to the type of specialist help they might need to sustain the level of care and support that a child might require to minimise the risk of a placement or adoption breakdown.

SECTION 1

CHAPTER **3**

The possible causes of wetting and soiling in children and young people

Physical causes

Some possible physical causes related to wetting and soiling are outlined below.

Hormonal imbalance
This can occur when a child is not producing enough of a hormone called **vasopressin**, which serves to slow down the body's production of urine at night. Low vasopressin levels mean that some children continue to produce large quantities of urine during the night.

Overactive bladder
A child may have an overactive bladder. You might see signs of this during the day if the child has to rush to the toilet, and needs to wee frequently.

Urinary tract infection

The problem could be caused by a child having a urinary tract infection (UTI). This is an infection that affects the bladder, kidneys and the tubes connected to them. UTIs in children are fairly common and are treated with antibiotics.

Diet

Some drinks (for example, fizzy drinks like coca cola, or tea and coffee) can stimulate the kidneys to produce more urine; they can also irritate the bladder.

Constipation

This can be linked to a poor diet due to neglect, although it is not always the cause. Some children are afraid of the toilet, particularly if they have been constipated before and have had pain when trying to pass stools. Constipation can lead to "bowel overflow" soiling and can also affect bladder function.

Emotional causes

I will now explore what I consider to be the main focus of this book: the potential underlying *emotional* causes for wetting and soiling in children and young people who have been adopted or are looked after.

This is a highly complex and emotive area for both children and young people and their carers or adoptive parents. In some circumstances, the issue can be quite easily identified and linked to an event or particularly stressful period in a child's life, for example, starting school or changing placement. However, in many cases there will not simply be one precipitating factor, but rather a multiplicity of issues that are contributing to the overall difficulty, which are likely to take some considerable time and a great deal of patience to unravel. Having said this, we must also accept that

13

we might never get to the root of the problem, but with help and support we might develop a deeper understanding about why it is happening.

As discussed earlier, children who have been removed from their families of origin will not have had consistent and reliable parenting or the benefit of the ordinary rudimentary building blocks to support their healthy physical and emotional development. Not having had an early experience of feeling safely held can impact on an infant's capacity to take in and hold on to good experiences. This can, in turn, leave them fearing that everyone and everything will be taken away, and sometimes this is expressed in a very concrete way. Soiling or urinating, or both, can become an entrenched habit born out of unmet needs. It may be an unconscious strategy to "remain a baby" in order to keep a parent close.

Children and young people in adverse circumstances may have become frightened of their caregivers and developed unhelpful ways of eliciting attention, which can result in disturbing or destructive behaviour. When children and young people have been removed from their families, whatever the reason, it is important to remember that although they may now be in a safe environment and out of "harm's way", as it were, they do not leave their trauma behind, but will continue to carry it with them, into every new situation. Often children who have experienced fragmented or traumatic early relationships are unable to differentiate between who is a safe and who is an unsafe adult. Maltreated children will have adapted to their early environment; they are likely to relate to new caregivers in the same ways as they related to their parents or other abusive adults in their lives, and it will take a long time, years even, for them to develop a capacity to trust.

On the following pages, I have listed some of the potential

emotional causes of wetting, soiling and smearing in children and young people. Many causes overlap, but it is a broad overview of the kinds of issues that arise and the possible underlying emotional causes that I hope will resonate with carers and adoptive parents who are trying to make sense of distressing situations.

Abuse

It is generally understood that many children or young people who have been removed from their family of origin and placed in local authority care, or who are adopted, will probably have experienced some degree of abuse and neglect, which may be, or may become, an underlying cause of toileting issues.

For ease of reference, I have outlined below definitions of emotional abuse, sexual abuse, physical abuse and neglect drawn from the UK Government guidance, *Working Together to Safeguard Children* (Department for Education, 2015). These definitions are not definitive but meant to act as a guide.

Sexual abuse: Sexual abuse involves forcing or enticing a child or young person to take part in sexual activities, including prostitution, whether the child is aware of what is happening or not. The activities may involve physical contact, including both penetrative and non-penetrative acts such as kissing, touching or fondling the child's genitals or breasts, vaginal or anal intercourse, or oral sex. Sexual abuse may also include non-contact activities, like inducing children to look at, or participate in, the production of pornographic material, or to watch sexual activities, or to behave in sexually inappropriate ways.

Emotional abuse: Emotional abuse is the persistent emotional maltreatment of a child, resulting in severe and persistent adverse effects on the child's emotional development. It may convey to children that they are worthless or unloved, inadequate, or valued only insofar as they meet the needs of another person. Emotional abuse may feature age- or developmentally-inappropriate expectations being imposed on children, including interactions that are beyond the child's developmental capability, as well as overprotection, which limits exploration and learning, and may prevent the child from participating in normal social activities. Emotional abuse may also involve seeing or hearing the ill-treatment of another, or it may involve serious bullying, causing children to feel frightened or in danger. Some level of emotional abuse is present in all types of maltreatment of a child, although it may occur alone.

Physical abuse: Physical abuse is hitting, shaking, throwing, poisoning, burning, scalding, drowning, suffocating, or otherwise causing physical harm to a child or failing to protect a child from that harm. Physical harm may also be caused when a parent or carer fabricates symptoms or deliberately induces illness in a child.

Neglect: Neglect is the persistent failure to meet a child's basic physical and/or psychological needs, resulting in serious impairment to the child's health or development. Neglect may occur during pregnancy due to maternal substance abuse. Once a child is born, a parent or carer may neglect to provide adequate food, clothing or shelter, abandon or fail to protect a child from physical and emotional harm or danger, or fail to ensure safe supervision and access to appropriate medical care. Neglect can also be unresponsiveness to a child's basic emotional needs.

There are very many concerning behaviours that are linked to emotional, physical and sexual abuse and neglect. Children and young people who have been abused will try to assert control over difficult aspects of their lives, for example, by holding on to their poo, by refusing to use the toilet, by soiling their underwear, or by smearing in inappropriate places. Soiling, in particular, is one of many stress-induced dysregulated behaviours, which could be the child's response to any of the above experiences of abuse.

If a child is not constipated and is soiling his pants or smearing faeces, the issue could be related to an emotional or psychological difficulty or upset, which will need to be considered.

However, one should not jump to conclusions that a child or young person has been sexually abused because they have started wetting, soiling or smearing, even if it has been identified as not being related to physical causes or a lack of toilet training. It is more helpful to consider the different aspects and nuances of the behaviour in the context of the child's or young person's developmental stage and current environment in order to gain a holistic overview of the difficulties.

Attention seeking

Sometimes foster carers and adoptive parents describe a child or young person's wetting, smearing and soiling as something that is done on purpose, perhaps as "attention seeking" behaviour. This might sound slightly negative, but that is exactly what it might be. I say this because experience has shown us that a child might consciously or unconsciously *draw attention* to a particular difficulty or experience, which they do not have the words to express. So, if a child is not constipated and is soiling his pants or smearing poo, the issue could be related to an emotional or psychological difficulty, which will need to be given careful consideration.

It is important therefore that carers and parents are helped to understand children's signals and to be aware that an infant or young person who has been neglected or abused is probably not acting in a deliberately defiant way, but may be relying on survival techniques they have developed to ward off perceived or real threats, or concretely evacuating difficult feelings that they are unable to process.

In my experience of working with looked after children, foster carers have often bravely prepared themselves, or at times sought to protect themselves, from the emotional and psychological "mess" that children who have been removed from their families might bring with them. But they are often not prepared for the concrete "physical mess" in the form of wetting, soiling and the smearing of various bodily fluids that could be thought about as a physical manifestation of their confused and frightened internal state.

Anxiety

Anxiety can lead to frequent urination; in younger children when physical control has not been established, this can lead to wetting accidents. However, a sudden onset of wetting after a sustained period of dryness, once physical causes have been ruled out, could be linked to a particularly stressful time in a child's life, for example, some children or young people in the general population may find that their bladder or bowels are affected as a result of exam anxiety, regardless of their background history. Children who are in care or who have been adopted may be struggling to adjust to a change of placement, or it could be an indication of abuse.

Comfort

A child who has been left in a dirty nappy for long periods might draw some comfort from being wet with poos, as it is what he is accustomed to. The smell of urine may also unconsciously remind the child of his previous family, or it may even be a way of trying to be offensive to keep others from getting close to him. In some circumstances, smearing becomes part of a routine that a child has developed from which he might draw comfort. Alternatively, the child may be seeking extra nurturing and comfort from a carer, and sees this as an acceptable way of eliciting it. One child soiled regularly at school, because when she did, her adoptive mother would miraculously appear at lunch time to bring a clean set of clothes.

Shame

Children who have experienced neglect whilst living with their birth families, due to a lack of supervision, parental mental illness or addiction to drugs and alcohol, may not have been toilet trained or taught to wipe their bottoms properly. They may feel anxious or ashamed about using the toilet. If they have been previously chastised or physically disciplined for having "accidents", children may associate using the toilet with punishment or harsh discipline.

Some children will not get up in the night to go to the toilet, because they have been used to their room being locked or have been forbidden to leave their room at night. When a child or young person experiences shameful feelings, he may resort to trying to keep other people at a distance out of fear that anyone who gets to know him will discover the "bad" or "shameful" feelings he has inside. Traumatised children can become highly skilled at making their carers feel useless, impotent, and thereby unconsciously recreating past experiences by provoking punitive feelings and responses, and thus reinforcing their sense of worthlessness.

Control

It is not at all unusual for young children to hold on to poos whilst at nursery or school, and it is a commonly reported issue in the general population, although this would be concerning if it continued for an extended period. However, a child who has a need to be in control may hold on to his poos to feel better about his underlying feelings of helplessness. Smearing can provide a sense of control over one's body and environment when other areas of life feel out of control, and it can also prevent unwanted social interaction.

Esteem

Being wet, smelly and repulsive may be a reflection of how a child feels about himself: that he does not deserve to take care

19

of himself or indeed be taken care of. Children sometimes have a smell that is unpleasant – this can come from an unconscious wish to keep others at a distance, or it could be the child communicating his sense of deprivation and lack of self-esteem. Foster carers and adoptive parents may have to cope with a child who exhibits repulsive behaviours such as farting, soiling or smearing as a means of keeping people away.

Anger

Children who find it difficult to regulate and articulate their feelings because they have not experienced a parent/carer who could help them to recognise, "contain" and manage their feelings from an early age, may communicate their anger and frustration by wetting, smearing or soiling as a means of concretely getting rid of difficult or unwanted feelings. This is a leaking out or evacuation of bad feelings because a child has not been helped to contain these feelings at a crucial earlier developmental stage.

The impact of transitions/separations/ unfamiliar surroundings

It is important to take into consideration the *context* in which the wetting and/or soiling is taking place. I have already said that wetting and soiling accidents are not unusual in the general population of children aged between four and seven, and can often be linked to stressful life events.

However, for children who have had very difficult early experiences, even activities that on the surface appear to be benign and pleasurable can stir up huge amounts of anxiety and provoke an extreme or adverse reaction. Transitions and separations can be difficult for all children to manage, regardless of their background, but they are particularly poignant for children who are, or have been, in the care system, and who will have experienced many transitions and separations about which they will have had very little warning and no control. They may have come to experience change in a visceral way, as being dropped, abandoned or rejected, regardless of the circumstances. Below I have outlined some examples of events that have been known to trigger a stress response in children. Again, this list is by no means exhaustive, but is meant to give an overview of the kind of situations that can cause a regression, which manifests itself by wetting or soiling:

- going on holiday;

- going on a school trip;

- staying with a friend overnight;

- meeting unfamiliar adults or professionals;

- starting or moving school;

- change of placement – there may be a regression in a child's behaviour if they move to a new placement or go to live with adoptive parents, for many different reasons, for example, a change in their night-time routine. They may be frightened of the dark or worried about asking for help in the night if they need to use the toilet for fear of being shouted at or told off;

- birth of a sibling;

- arrival of a new foster/adoptive sibling in the family;

- parental separation;

- parental illness;

- bereavement;

- any change in routine;

- contact – I make this last point with some caution.

21

It is not that contact causes these difficulties, but for the purpose of this book I am highlighting the issue of contact because, inevitably, contact with birth parents or siblings that a child or young person is no longer living with, whatever the reason, can stir up many conflicting feelings that will be hard to process, and very few children will have the emotional language to articulate.

CHAPTER 4

Parental expectations

When a child is taken into foster care, moves placement, or goes to live with an adoptive family, he will have needs that are over and above those of other children of a similar age. It is important therefore not to make assumptions – for example, that because a child is a certain age, he will have been potty trained. Just because chronologically it makes sense, the reality might have been very different.

The issue of parental expectations relates to the experience of the child in his birth family as well as in his foster or adoptive family. Birth parents who have been preoccupied with physical or mental ill health issues, difficulties related to substance misuse, or domestic violence, may not have been emotionally available to pay attention to their child's developmental needs or to tend to their toilet training. Social workers, and subsequently foster carers or adopters, may be advised by birth parents that children have been potty trained and that there are no issues relating to their toileting needs. This information can then follow children around their various placements in official documentation. Sadly, birth parents' narratives cannot always be relied upon and can arouse false expectations.

Children who have experienced neglectful parenting, or who have had a lack of parental supervision, will neither be accustomed to having their basic needs met, nor will they have developed a sense of hope that they will be helped by adults. These children often become "self-reliant" – they rely on their own, usually very limited, underdeveloped and impoverished resources to meet their needs rather than trust an adult to do so.

For example, children aged four, five or six, who are left to feed or change their much younger siblings, may not have been toilet trained themselves. Such children often come across as being quite "pseudo-mature" or "over-parentified". Because they have had to manage themselves and assume roles and responsibilities that are inappropriate for their age, they can appear more capable and "older than their years". When faced with a child whose life experience ages them beyond their chronological age, there is a risk that professionals and foster carers or adoptive parents are drawn into assuming that they are far more independent and able to manage their personal hygiene and toileting than they actually are.

It might be difficult to comprehend that an eight, nine or ten-year-old has not grasped the basics of toilet training. So whilst it is important to hold in mind that wetting and/or soiling could be linked to abuse or other traumas in the child's life, it is equally important not to make premature assumptions, but to explore, in a sensitive way, with the child, what might be going on and what help they have had in this area.

Nature and extent of the problem

Issues relating to wetting, soiling or smearing can feel embarrassing to talk about. Some carers or adoptive parents may think that it is something they should be able to manage within the family, and the problem can remain hidden and go untreated until it becomes overwhelming.

A request for help by carers or adoptive parents will usually be made only after some considerable effort has already been put into trying to resolve the difficulty. Some carers or adoptive parents may feel that they have failed both themselves and their child in some way. Others may feel uncomfortable about discussing such a personal matter. Many have reported feeling confused about the different medical terminology applied to the various issues. Therefore, it is important for professionals to be non-judgemental and to use straightforward and accessible language. It is also vital to acknowledge that carers and adoptive parents have a lot to contribute based on their own knowledge and experience of their child. Emotions can become very highly charged when carers are distressed, frustrated and worn out, and when there is a real risk that the placement will break down if the problem is not fixed.

Can the carer/adoptive parent give a description of the problem?

In the first instance, it is important that carers or parents are encouraged to give as full and comprehensive a history of the problem as they can. The quality of the information that you, as a carer or adoptive parent, are able to provide will depend on the length of time that the child has been in your care and the quality of your relationship with him.

Birth children who are experiencing toileting problems have usually had the benefit of a parent who is able to give a coherent narrative of their early life and developmental milestones, but depending on the age of the child when taken into care, their background history can sometimes be piecemeal and fragmented, especially if there have been several changes of placement. There may be conflicting reports depending on the source of information and different interpretations may have been made.

Even in the most ordinary of circumstances, it can be a struggle to provide a description of the difficulty, but it is important to try and get the facts straight in order to develop a holistic overview. This can be quite straightforward for infants, but older children such as those in their primary school years may be more secretive due to feelings of shame or a fear of being disciplined or humiliated if this has been their experience prior to being taken into care. It is likely to be even harder in the case of adolescents, who are expected to need less practical support with their personal care and may feel more inhibited and embarrassed about disclosing their difficulties.

Unravelling the description

To start with, it is necessary to assess the size and nature of the problem: what exactly is the child or young person doing? I have listed some of the specific potential questions below:

- How long has it been going on?
- What is the exact nature of the problem?
- Is he incontinent during the day? How often?
- Does he do a full wee in his pants?
- Does he do a partial wee in his pants?
- Does he have damp pants?
- Is he not making it to the toilet on time?
- Is he weeing in different locations?
- Is he wetting the bed at night?

- Is he doing a big poo in his pants? How often?

- Does he start a poo in his pants and have to be encouraged to go to the toilet?

- Does he have dirty marks ("skid marks") in his pants?

- Is he smearing his poo?

- Do younger children only do a poo in their nappy and resist toilet training?

- As far as the carer/parent is aware, is there a discernible trigger?

- Does the regressive behaviour occur before certain events, such as a change of placement, a school trip, change in contact arrangements, a sleepover at a friend's house?

Daytime wetting (enuresis)

Daytime wetting can occur by itself or when a child is also bedwetting. This problem can be very stressful or embarrassing for children when they go to school, as it can lead to teasing or bullying.

Helpful questions to consider include:

- Does the child forget to use the toilet when he is playing or otherwise absorbed? Does the child leave it too late?

- Is the child always in a hurry in the toilet and consequently does not completely empty his bladder?

- What are the child's drinking habits?

- Are there concerns about other areas of the child's development?

SECTION 1

Bedwetting at night (nocturnal enuresis)

Helpful questions to consider include:

- Are there any other concerns about the child's development?

- Is the child very tired and sleeping deeply, and thus not able to wake up when his bladder is full?

- Is the child drinking a lot of fluids before bedtime?

- Is the child constipated? Constipation can place pressure on the bladder, thereby reducing the amount of urine it is able to hold.

Soiling (encopresis)

This is viewed as being relatively normal in toddlers and younger children as they gradually learn to control their bowels. Under normal circumstances, healthy children will develop control over their bowels by about the age of four.

Helpful questions to consider include:

- Do you have any information about the child's previous toilet habits and routines?

- Has the child had a change of diet?

- Is the child taking any medication that might affect his bowels?

- Is there any sign that the child might be constipated?

- Does the child seem to know when he needs a poo?

- Does he seem to know when and how to use the toilet?

It is very important to consider whether a child is constipated. Frequency of bowel movements is variable, but children should have at least four poos a week, and should not need to strain to poo. Hard or very large poos can also be a sign of constipation (see ERIC website at www.eric.org.uk for more details of constipation).

Constipation involves the bowel becoming blocked with hard poo. The child finds it difficult to pass the poo and liquid poo may then leak out around the blockage, which can leave stains on clothes, known as "overflow" or more commonly referred to as "skid marks". The child can start to link pain with pooing as a result and will sometimes hold in his poo, especially if he has had a hard poo in the past that caused a small split in the anus, called a fissure, which can be extremely painful.

SECTION I

CHAPTER **5**

Who is this a problem for and whom does it affect?

Foster carers and adoptive parents

Whatever the issue, be it persistent bedwetting, soiling or smearing, it is likely to have a significant impact on the child, adoptive parents, foster carers, siblings, the wider family and school. Depending on the severity of the problem, it is likely to affect outings and other family activities, or opportunities for sleepovers, and it can become the cause of great resentment and frustration. The increased laundry may be stressful for a busy household and have a financial impact.

The child

Is the child or young person upset or distressed by the issue? Do they make a good job of hiding their feelings? Children who have not had an experience of being held in mind by their primary caregivers, or who have little expectation that their needs will be met, are very adept at trying to manage on their own and protecting themselves from feeling vulnerable. They will therefore find the idea of trusting an adult to support them in such a personal matter extremely difficult, and it is likely to take some considerable time before sufficient trust is developed to make them feel safe enough to begin to talk about the problem, let alone tackle it. They may feel stigmatised by the problem, experience bullying, and become angry, withdrawn and/or depressed as a result of being teased and feeling humiliated. They may feel unable to participate in activities or to join clubs.

Studies have highlighted that children who experience encopresis have more anxiety and depression symptoms, difficulties with attention, more social and behavioural problems and lower levels of academic performance (Mosca and Schatz, 2013).

School

If problems occur in school, there may be practical issues to resolve.

- Can the child ask to go to the toilet at any time without being questioned?

- Is the toilet easily accessible?

- Are there regular toilet breaks for all the children?

- How are "accidents" dealt with?

It can be helpful if your child's teachers are made aware of the situation at home, so that they can work together with you to provide a consistent response to the child that protects their dignity.

31

What can carers/adoptive parents do to help?

On an emotional level

- Talk to your child. The way in which you approach the issue with your child is extremely important and will vary according to their age and level of understanding. It is a difficult task and it will be hard to maintain a balance. Carers and adoptive parents may be tempted to ask a child why they wet/soil/smear, which will often prove fruitless because the child may have no idea himself why he does it, nor feel in control of the situation. Putting pressure on a child or young person to give an explanation about why they are wetting/soiling/smearing is likely to increase their anxiety and potentially exacerbate the problem.

- Try and get a sense of the child's or young person's *individual* experience of the difficulty and how it might be linked to their emotional experience, and hold in mind that it is not "a one size fits all" situation.

- With younger children, try using the same language that they use, for example, "wees" and "poos", whereas older children may feel more comfortable using more grown-up words. Identify and agree what language is used within the family. Being aware of how children or young people refer to their bodily functions signals to them that you are interested in understanding their experience of the problem, and this may help them to feel less embarrassed to talk about it.

- It is important for carers and adoptive parents to involve the child or young person in a way that makes them feel safe and understood rather than blamed, ashamed or humiliated. I am aware that this is likely to be more difficult to achieve with looked after or adopted children, who by virtue of their past experiences may not respond to the most sensitive and encouraging of parental efforts.

- Some children will respond well to gentle encouragement and the implementation of simple routines or reward charts (see further detail in later section), and plenty of praise to increase their self-esteem. Others may feel threatened or deeply persecuted by your interest and genuine offers of support, and are therefore likely to challenge or provoke you for raising the issue. Those who are well versed in secrecy may try and hide it or deny that there is a problem at all, despite it being glaringly obvious, which is likely to challenge even the most patient of carers. Having said this and acknowledging that the issue is likely to cause carers and parents some considerable distress and frustration, try not to get angry or shout as this will add to the child's level of anxiety and more than likely make the problem worse.

- Carers and adoptive parents can support their child by explaining that they want to help them to tackle the problem. Depending on your child's age, include their view on how best they might manage the situation in order to enable them to gain more control over their own bodies.

On a practical level

- Adopt a calm, straightforward tone and encourage the child to take age-appropriate responsibility for managing wet bedding and clothing. You could prepare clean night clothes and bedlinen for older children who can then be encouraged to change their bed and put the soiled bedding in the laundry.

- Avoid sharing laundry baskets, as this can cause embarrassment.

- Remind your child to take a bath or shower so that they do not smell, and risk being bullied or teased. Allow extra time in the morning rush.

- Provide changes of clothes and a plan for situations when your child is not with you.

- Encourage your child to drink lots of water during the day as this helps the bladder to fill properly. He should also be encouraged to eat food that is rich in fibre, such as fruit, vegetables and whole grains, which will make the poo softer and easier to pass.

- Breakfast is an important meal, and a warm drink first thing in the morning can help a child to use the toilet before school.

- If a child is soiling because he has never been helped to establish a toileting routine, encourage him to develop a regular routine by praising him for his effort and any successes.

- Make sure that your child has the opportunity for lots of activity and regular exercise to help the poo move through the intestine and reduce the risk of constipation.

- Check out whether anyone has shown your child how to wipe himself after going to the toilet. If he is too old or too vulnerable to have you show him, you could perhaps use a teddy to demonstrate.

- Encourage your child to go to the toilet as soon as he gets the urge, and monitor him for hard or painful poos or signs that he may be holding his poo in, or seems afraid to use the toilet.

- Model the behaviour of going to the toilet when you need to, by telling your child why you are going to the bathroom.

- Reduce your child's fluid intake right before bedtime (at most a small cup). Teach your child to avoid drinks that include caffeine, such as coca cola, tea or coffee, because they stimulate the kidneys and lead to more urine being produced.

- Make going to the toilet an enjoyable part of your child's bedtime routine and encourage him to stay long enough to fully empty his bladder.

- Leave a light on in the bathroom or hallway at night, or make a torch available for children who may be afraid of the dark. Some children may previously have been punished for getting up in the night. Let them know that it is OK to call you if they wake up and need help going to the toilet.

- Ensure that there is privacy in the bathroom.

- You could consider establishing a positive reward system using sticker charts. The rewards should be for behaviour that supports positive changes, as opposed to having a dry bed/clean pants. This motivational type of approach can work for younger children; rewards may be given for drinking recommended levels of fluid during the day and using the toilet to pass urine before going to sleep.

SECTION I

- Spend some time together making a diary or chart to help you and your child see when he has wetting or soiling accidents. This kind of activity will reinforce your relationship with your child by enabling him to take some responsibility, whilst giving the message that trying to manage the problem is a shared task. Talk with your child about getting up a bit earlier in the mornings in order to enable him to have time to relax on the toilet before going to school.

- You could use mattress, duvet and pillow protectors, and absorbent sheets – but make sure the bed is still comfortable. Some parents/carers find it helpful to use waterproof sleeping bag liners for sleepovers so that their child does not miss out on opportunities to spend time and have fun with friends. Depending on his age and level of ability, support your child to manage independently, for example, a child who wets the bed might find it helpful to have a "pull up" to wear at night.

- Check the bed each morning rather than asking your child if he has wet the bed (this could inadvertently add to his feelings of shame and humiliation). Remove soiled or wet items and take a calm and neutral approach to changing the bed, perhaps with his help.

- Try to be fairly open in the family with conversations about using the toilet. Humour can be helpful.

- Make family trips to the toilet while out and about: 'Let's stop to use the toilet here', rather than continually reminding one child and thereby drawing attention to him.

- Don't talk to others about the issue in front of your child, unless you have first agreed with him that it is appropriate.

36

- Overall, difficult though it is, parents who are able to accept that their child is not going to be able to stop wetting, soiling or smearing quickly, or without a great deal of patience and support, are more likely to be able to manage and contain the problem than those who put pressure on children to stop.

This is a lot to ask of carers and adoptive parents, so it is important to know where to access support for you and your child.

SECTION 1

CHAPTER **6**

Where and when to get help

When foster carers and adoptive parents have tried and exhausted the suggestions outlined in the previous chapter, and probably more, it is important to know where next to turn for help. In the first instance, it is advisable to seek support from your GP, who will be able to signpost you to appropriate services for an assessment of your child's specific difficulties. Support services for bladder and bowel problems vary a great deal across the UK, but you may be referred to a **paediatrician**, the school nursing service, a **continence nurse** or a LAC (looked after children) nurse. The LAC nurse will have a great deal of experience in this area and can provide expert help as well as appropriate signposting. These healthcare professionals are usually based in GP practices, clinics in the community or in hospitals.

BUT: see your GP straight away if your child shows any sign of a urinary infection, such as pain or irritation when passing urine, an urgent need to pass urine, or if the urine is smelly. **OR:** if your child is constipated, or has offensive stools or diarrhoea.

Bedwetting (nocturnal enuresis)

Assessment

According to NICE guidance (2010a), it is good practice to consider children for treatment for bedwetting when they reach five years of age. Prior to this, help and advice can be obtained from health visitors and school nurses.

Children presenting with bedwetting issues will need a thorough and comprehensive assessment, which should be undertaken by an appropriate healthcare professional to pinpoint any medical, emotional or physical symptoms or triggers, and to consider whether further assessment and/or treatment are required.

There are two types of bedwetting:

1. **Primary bedwetting** – refers to bedwetting that has been going on since early childhood without a break, for example, a child who has never been dry at night for any significant period.

2. **Secondary bedwetting** – refers to bedwetting that starts again after the child has been dry at night for a significant length of time (at least six months). A child with secondary bedwetting is more likely to have other symptoms such as daytime wetting, and it can be an indication of either a medical condition or an emotional problem.

What might you be asked about your child during an assessment?

You will be asked to give a full background and developmental history, including information about pregnancy and birth and

39

whether there have been any genetic issues. Bedwetting can run in families; if one birth parent has been known to wet the bed as a child, it is more likely that their child will wet the bed, and this likelihood increases if both parents wet the bed as children. The assessment can be distressing if collating a coherent background history is not possible because the information about birth parents is too sparse. It might be advisable to contact the health professional in advance to explain your child's history. You will also be asked:

- How did your child react to toilet training?

- What is the pattern of your child's bedwetting? For example, how many nights a week and how many times a night does it occur?

- How much urine is there?

- What times of night does the bedwetting occur?

- Does your child wake up after wetting?

- Does your child experience any daytime symptoms?

- How often does your child pass urine during the day?

- Does your child have a sense of urgency about using the toilet?

- Does your child experience pain when weeing?

- Is there a discernible pattern? For example, do daytime symptoms only occur in certain situations?

- Does your child avoid using the toilet at school or in other settings?

- Does your child have any diagnosed medical conditions or take any medication?

- Are there any relevant stress factors?

- Are there any concerns about general behaviour?

- Are there any diagnosed developmental difficulties?

- What is your child's normal diet?

- What is your child's bedtime routine?

Your child may have to undergo routine tests to rule out any urinary tract infection (UTI) or kidney/bladder malfunction.

What treatment could your child be offered?

There are different methods and treatments to support children to stay dry at night.

Alarms

Following assessment, an alarm system may be considered appropriate, if you and your child are motivated to use it. A bedwetting alarm consists of a small sensor and alarm, which are attached to your child's nightclothes. When the sensor starts to get wet, it sets off the alarm. It is worth noting that vibrating alarms are also available for children who have a hearing impairment. Over time, the alarm should help children to recognise when they need to wake up and use the toilet because their bladder is full.

Medication

If, after some perseverance, the bedwetting does not respond to the alarm treatment, your child could be offered a medication called **desmopressin**. Desmopressin is a synthetic (man-made) version of vasopressin, which is the hormone that regulates the production of urine. It helps to reduce the amount of urine produced by the kidneys. This is prescribed and monitored by health professionals.

NICE guidance (2010a) indicates that when bedwetting has not responded to treatment with an alarm or desmopressin, children should be referred to a healthcare professional with expertise in prescribing **anticholinergics** in combination with desmopressin. Anticholinergic medication relaxes the muscles of the bladder. This in turn can help improve its capacity and reduce your child's urge to wee during the night.

If all the above treatment options have not been effective, **trycyclics** (imipramine) may be used. Imipramine also relaxes the muscles of the bladder to increase its capacity and reduce the urge to urinate.

Daytime wetting (diurnal enuresis)

Assessment

It is helpful to take a diary of daytime wetting accidents with you to the appointment. This would include:

- a record of the incidents;
- how much fluid your child drinks;
- the amount of wee he passes;
- how often he manages to use the toilet.

You will be asked about your child's general health and development, and whether there have been any night time wetting accidents or if he is constipated. You may be asked to help your child to measure his bladder capacity (this is the amount of urine the bladder can hold when it is full) by passing urine into a jug. Your child may be given a routine urine test to rule out possible infection. Your child may also need an ultrasound scan or x-ray to check the bladder and kidneys.

If the difficulty persists, or your child has repeated urinary tract infections, or when wetting starts in an older child who has not

42

previously experienced any wetting accidents, further tests may be required. These include **urodynamic tests**, to check how the bladder is filling up and emptying, and **cystometry**, which examines the bladder activity.

What treatment could your child be offered?

Your child may be given a programme of using the toilet at regular intervals during the day while increasing his fluid intake. For example, you may be asked to encourage your child to wee on a timed basis *before* feeling the urge. This allows the bladder to empty while the outlet valve is still relaxed. It is important to time this carefully, especially if your child is going to school.

You may be asked to encourage your child to remain on the toilet after a wee, to count to 20 and try to wee again, which reduces any leftover urine in the bladder.

Constipation could be the cause of your child's daytime wetting accidents. This is because a bowel that is full of poo puts pressure on the bladder which becomes squashed and struggles to expand fully to hold lots of wee. As a result, your child feels the urge to urinate frequently and has to do lots of little wees. Treatment of the constipation in these cases will alleviate the issue.

Medication

Your child could be prescribed antibiotics if he has a urinary tract infection.

A medication called **oxybutynin** may be prescribed to relax the bladder muscle whilst the bladder is filling up, which enables it to hold more urine.

If your doctor suspects that the issue has an emotional or psychological cause, your child may be referred for help in this area.

SECTION I

SECTION I

Soiling (encopresis)

Children and young people who have been used to looking after themselves may have some deeply ingrained ways of managing, which can include smearing or hiding their poo in various locations around the house. This can be extremely frustrating and difficult for carers and adopters to manage.

There are two basic categories of encopresis:

1. **Primary encopresis** – refers to children who have never attained bowel control.

2. **Secondary encopresis** – refers to soiling after the child has successfully achieved bowel control.

Interestingly, it is reported that boys are five times more likely to present with encopresis than girls; children with neurodevelopmental disorders are also more likely to have this problem, and I will explore this later in the chapter.

Causes

Severe constipation can cause "**faecal impaction**", when a big poo or a build-up of poo gets stuck and blocks the rectum. This can lead to faecal soiling: small bits of poo break off into the child's pants or soft runny poo leaks out around the impacted mass in the rectum. As a result, soiling can often be mistaken for diarrhoea. The experience of pain whilst trying to poo is an important factor in constipation; withholding behaviours to prevent passage of painful poo is often confused with straining to pass poo.

The exact cause of constipation is not fully understood, but factors that contribute to it include pain, fever, dehydration, diet and fluid intake, psychological issues, toilet training, side effects of certain medicines, and familial history of constipation. If the signs and symptoms of constipation are not recognised, the link between soiling and constipation may be missed.

Constipation is called "**idiopathic constipation**" if it cannot be explained by anatomical or physiological abnormalities. The signs and symptoms of childhood idiopathic constipation include: infrequent bowel activity; foul smelling wind and poo; excessive wind; irregular texture; passing occasional enormous poos or frequent small pellets; withholding or straining to stop the passage of poo; soiling or overflow; abdominal pain; distension of the abdomen or discomfort; poor appetite; lack of energy; unhappy, angry or irritable moods; and general malaise (NICE, 2010b). In some cases, the intestines may become so enlarged as a result of being blocked with faeces that a child loses the sensation of needing to poo.

Assessment

As for bedwetting, if you are referred by your GP to a specialist, a thorough assessment will be undertaken. You will be asked about the type of symptoms your child is experiencing and to describe patterns related to their toileting habits:

- How often does your child poo?

- What symptoms has your child been showing? For example, what is the consistency of his poo? Is he doing large poos that sometimes block the toilet or hard pellets like rabbit droppings? (It is a good idea to become familiar with the Bristol stool chart – see www.eric.org.uk for more information.)

- Does your child have abdominal pain when he poos?

- How is his appetite? Is he drinking enough fluids and eating enough fruit and vegetables?

- How many times a week does he have a poo?

45

- Has he experienced any previous episodes of constipation or had an anal fissure?

- Are his bowel movements painful? Does he strain?

- Has he bled when passing poo?

- Has he exhibited retentive posturing (a typical straight-legged, tiptoed, back arching posture)?

What treatment could your child be offered?

A medical examination and a scan could rule out the presence of any organic causes.

If your child is constipated, a doctor should prescribe a **laxative** to ease the passage of the hardened stool through the rectum. Once the stool has passed, further laxatives may be used to empty the colon regularly and decrease painful bowel movements.

You may also be offered advice about how to change your child's diet in order to encourage easier bowel movements.

Support

Many children and young people experience social, psychological and educational consequences due to wetting and soiling that require prolonged support. As a carer or parent of a child who is wetting or soiling, it can be very difficult to know where else or who you can turn to for advice and support.

NICE guidance suggests that parents and carers should be offered support and assistance as they may be experiencing difficulties coping (emotionally, financially and logistically) with the burden of soiling and smearing, and may therefore be expressing anger or negativity towards the child. Assistance could take the form of practical and/or financial help to purchase some special items, or to cope with laundry bills; and emotional support by providing a sounding board to vent understandable frustration and distress. Support could come from the supervising social worker or post-adoption service.

It is important to hold in mind that even when there is a *physical* explanation for the difficulty, it can still take a long time to resolve. In some cases, if the problem is particularly entrenched or longstanding, it may require long-term management, making full use of all the support that is available.

If physical causes have been explored and ruled out, the difficulty could be linked to stress or anxiety and may be alleviated quite quickly if the source of the problem is easily identified.

What can you do if the above strategies don't work?

Both research and experience show that wetting, soiling and smearing problems may be linked to more profound deep-seated psychological difficulties related to the quality of children's earlier experiences of abuse and/or their disrupted attachments.

Children who are fostered or adopted will often experience what is referred to as **comorbidity**. This means that they might present a number of different difficulties that co-exist alongside one another and affect their behaviour and overall functioning, which can make ordinary everyday life very hard to manage. In these cases, the cause will be far more complex to identify and treat than if the child or young person was presenting with one clearly defined disorder or problem. This can feel very frustrating for carers and adoptive parents who are struggling to cope and are desperate for a resolution, but understanding what children

SECTION 1

47

may be communicating through their behaviour, and why, is essential. Therefore, if the problem is particularly persistent and other strategies have been tried, it would be best to seek further support and advice from your GP, who can refer you for more specialist psychological support to **CAMHS**. (If children are "looked after", there may be a specific referral path to CAMHS; the child's social worker should be able to advise.)

CAMHS

What is CAMHS?

CAMHS (Child and Adolescent Mental Health Services) is an NHS (National Health Service) mental health provision that focuses on the emotional needs and well-being of children and young people. CAMHS specialists may work with the whole family or with children and adolescents alone; sometimes they work with adolescents in groups. Individual therapy can be especially helpful for children who have been sexually abused, or who have experienced severe trauma. Children who have suffered serious abuse or neglect can be difficult to care for, and the right agencies can offer support and advice to parents and carers as well as to children and young people.

CAMHS consists of **multidisciplinary** teams that include some or all of the following professionals:

- psychiatrists;
- psychologists;
- social workers;
- nurses;
- support workers;

- occupational therapists;

- psychological therapists – this may include child psychotherapists, family psychotherapists, play therapists, cognitive behavioural therapists, and creative art therapists;

- primary mental health link workers;

- specialist substance misuse workers.

Who can refer to CAMHS?

Your GP, health visitor, paediatrician, school nurse, LAC nurse, educational psychologist or SENCO (Special Educational Needs Co-ordinator in school), social worker or supervising social worker can refer you to CAMHS. You can also make a self-referral.

In some areas, CAMHS provides a range of specialist interventions as well as support for children in care and adopted children and young people, foster carers, adoptive parents, kinship carers, social workers, and the wider network.

The need for post-adoption support is recognised in the Adoption and Children Act 2002, but provision is patchy, and it can be challenging to find the most appropriate assessments and interventions for this population. It is important to note that although CAMHS exist across the UK, what is offered will vary from location to location depending on the resources available in that particular area. The threshold for accepting referrals will also differ; some services will be able to offer an appointment quite quickly, whereas in other areas families may have to wait a long time for an assessment and treatment.

What to expect?

Some CAMHS professionals, for example, child and adolescent psychotherapists, clinical psychologists and family therapists, are specially trained to provide different types of talking therapies.

They may want to see you together with your child in the first instance. You may be asked a lot of questions about your family and background. Some adopters and carers question why this is relevant when it is not their birth child who is exhibiting the problem, but these are important areas to explore in order for professionals to develop a good understanding of the context of the difficulty, and how you and other family members view it and respond to it. Professionals are mindful that foster carers and adoptive parents are having to manage complex emotions relating to their child's current and past experiences as well as distressing feelings that may be evoked in themselves as a result. They will be interested in how you respond to the day-to-day challenges of parenting, and what you feel has worked or not worked previously.

Having space and time to make sense of a child's behaviour and expectations, to share worries and frustrations and the impact they have on families, as well as to acknowledge achievements, can be invaluable. This process can take time because carers, adoptive parents, social workers and the child or young person might have different points of view about the cause and severity of the problem and possible solutions, or even about whether there is a problem at all!

Once they have a good sense of the difficulties, the professionals will discuss with you and your child, and if appropriate the wider network, the different strategies that can help, and you will decide together what to do next. Because children can be managing hugely complex and multi-faceted issues, there is no "one size fits all" treatment available.

Holding in mind that services available across the UK will differ, you could be offered one of a range of interventions and/ or advised to access more practical support – for example, a parenting group might be able to help you to develop strategies to manage the challenges of parenting a child with complex needs either before or alongside a therapeutic intervention.

Different types of therapy

Psychoanalytic child psychotherapy

Child and adolescent psychotherapists are committed to understanding the complex emotional lives of infants, children, young people, families and carers. They work within a **psychoanalytic** framework, which looks beneath the surface of problematic emotions, behaviours or relationships in order to help children, young people and their families to develop a better understanding of themselves and their difficulties. The problems identified in a present relationship can lead to an understanding of difficulties experienced in previous relationships in the child's life.

Child and adolescent psychotherapists are trained to observe a child or young person and respond to what they might be communicating through their behaviour and play. During a therapeutic session, younger children may be encouraged to play, while older children may be asked to draw or paint, and adolescents to talk about their feelings. Child and adolescent psychotherapists share their observations and thoughts with the child, thereby affirming that his *own* thoughts and difficulties are being taken seriously and understood in the context of the therapeutic relationship. It is important that the setting feels safe and consistent, and therefore sessions take place on the same day and time each week. Over time, the child or adolescent can begin to recognise, and to express confused, frightened, hurt, angry or painful feelings, which can then gradually be put into words rather than actions, so that emotions can be expressed in less disturbed ways.

51

Child and adolescent psychotherapists may see children and young people on their own or with other family members. Foster carers and adopters often struggle with children who seek to reject and undermine their placements because unpredictability and instability are all they have experienced. That is why they are usually offered parenting sessions alongside the child's individual sessions.

Cognitive behavioural therapy

Cognitive behavioural therapy (CBT) is a talking therapy based on the theory that thoughts, emotions, what we do and how our body feels are all connected. If we change one aspect, we can effect change in the other areas. CBT has a good evidence base for a wide range of mental health problems in children and young people.

When we feel worried or distressed, we often fall into patterns of thinking and responding that can make us feel even worse. CBT offers strategies in the here and now to help us notice and change unhelpful thinking styles or behaviour patterns so that we can feel better.

Family therapy

Family and systemic psychotherapy – often called family therapy – helps people in close relationships to help each other. It enables family members to express and explore difficult thoughts and emotions safely, to understand each other's experiences and views, appreciate each other's needs, build on family strengths, and make useful changes in their relationships and their lives. The aim is not to take sides, blame, or provide simple answers, but to engage family members in sharing understanding and exploring ways forward that work for them. This can be particularly helpful in complicated family situations where more time is needed to find solutions that work for all members.

Neurodevelopmental disorders

Wetting, soiling and smearing are also issues that are prevalent in children who have **neurodevelopmental disorders**. Children who are looked after or adopted have a higher rate of neurodevelopmental disorders than those living in their birth families (Ford et al, 2007). The data in the research cited here revealed significantly elevated rates of common disorders such as **ADHD**, learning difficulties and other neurodevelopmental disorders compared with children living in birth families, including those disadvantaged by high levels of social and economic adversity. Examples of neurodevelopmental disorders in children include attention-deficit/hyperactivity disorder (ADHD), **autism**, **learning disabilities**, **conduct disorders**, **cerebral palsy** and impaired vision and hearing.

When constipation or withholding poo, which is of normal consistency, is not an issue for a child, but he poos at times and in places that are inappropriate, then this could be related to developmental disorders such as oppositional defiant disorder or conduct disorder. Children who present with oppositional defiant disorder or conduct disorder (i.e. children who are intentionally defiant and non-compliant with parents and caregivers) may use inappropriate soiling as a form of retaliation to communicate their anger or as an attention-seeking strategy.

Some children and young people with physical disabilities, such as cerebral palsy, are more prone to idiopathic constipation as a result of impaired mobility. Children and young people with **Down's syndrome** or autism are also more prone to develop this condition. It is vital to access an early assessment and ongoing management plan for these children.

Dr Matt Woolgar, a consultant clinical psychologist at the South London and Maudsley NHS Trust, has undertaken some interesting research that has highlighted the tendency to over-diagnose

SECTION 1

attachment disorders in adopted and fostered children: he suggests that more common diagnoses such as ADHD, conduct disorder, **PTSD** or adjustment disorder should be considered in the first instance (Woolgar and Baldock, 2015). In conclusion, he recommends that services for looked after and adopted children should offer multidisciplinary assessments by specialist teams with expertise in the wide range of problems likely to present, including neurodevelopmental and **neuropsychological** problems. Woolgar recommends identifying and treating these common problems with evidence-based approaches, for example, CBT or parenting groups.

Mental health interventions specifically for attachment disorders in looked after or adopted children remain in the earliest stages of development (Buckner *et al*, 2008), and the best evidenced treatment is the promotion of stable placements with sensitive carers (Rutter *et al*, 2009; Zeanah *et al*, 2011). Therefore, whatever intervention is offered, foster carers and adoptive parents are a hugely valued and important resource in their own right. Their capacity to offer sensitive, reparative parenting remains pivotal to the development of children and young people, but they need to be well supported to maintain the level of resilience necessary to manage significant provocation.

CHAPTER 7

Cultural issues

Families may have different routines when it comes to toileting habits, which may or may not be linked to their own cultural and ethnic backgrounds, as well as their own expectations as adoptive parents and carers which have been highlighted earlier in this book. Some cultures are very private, and foster carers or adoptive parents might not feel comfortable talking about toileting habits, whereas others might not mind at all.

Whilst it is, of course, important to respect difference, a "culture clash" between families could present difficulties for children and young people who have to move from one placement to another, if their established body and toileting routine does not fit in with the next family's culture of using the bathroom. This can add to their sense of confusion and disorientation and exacerbate or even create a toileting problem. In such cases, a problem might be more linked to the routine of the foster or adoptive family rather than to the child and could be resolved quite quickly rather than requiring further investigation. This is especially so if there is an assumption that a child has been toilet trained at an earlier age when this is not necessarily the case.

Expectations of development, including the way and age in which children are toilet trained, will undoubtedly have an impact on adoptive parents' and foster carers' interactions with their children.

A child might find it difficult to negotiate the routine or practice of their adoptive family if it is very different from the culture they have known so far. These are matters that, of course, need to be understood and treated with sensitivity, but with perseverance and openness can be quite easily managed. Cross-cultural adopters might find it helpful to learn about attachment behaviour and toileting in their child's birth culture.

It is important that you familiarise yourself with all of the cultural differences for your child. For example, Muslims may prefer a shower to a bath because they are required to wash under running water. Cleanliness is very important for religious reasons – most Muslims do not consider that toilet paper is adequate for personal hygiene and prefer to wash with water. Therefore, depending on his age and background, it could be helpful to ask a Muslim child if he would like a jug of water in the bathroom in order to attend to his personal hygiene after using the toilet.

CHAPTER 8

Safeguarding concerns

Aware of the abuse and neglect that children might have experienced, foster carers and adoptive parents may well be understandably concerned and anxious about safeguarding issues and the need to protect themselves. Whereas they might feel safe in caring intimately for their own child, for example, wiping his bottom, they might feel less comfortable about being in the bathroom with a child who has previously had their privacy invaded. While respecting the child's personal space, subtle differences or difficulties he is experiencing may be overlooked.

It is vital that children feel safe, and although this is likely to take some time, that they are helped to accept you as an adult who can be trusted and who is available to meet all aspects of their physical care needs, especially if they have been abused and might harbour feelings of shame, fear or humiliation.

Be interested and try and talk to your child in an ordinary, straightforward way about your concerns or what you have noticed, and your willingness to try and help, whilst acknowledging that problems might take a while to sort out. Encourage them to think with you about how they might feel comfortable about communicating any toileting difficulties (e.g. they could draw a picture or write it down), so that you can think together about what might help.

Asking your child if they would like some help in the bathroom or knocking on their door are very straightforward ways of signalling your respect for their dignity and privacy, whilst also sending a strong message that boundaries are important and that they have some control over their personal space. This might serve to encourage children who are secretive and self-reliant to ask for more support, and to children who are disinhibited or at risk of exploitation, it sends a strong message that it is important to seek their permission to go into their personal space.

Conclusion

And finally: Below is a summary of the advice laid out in Section I of this book.

Do:

- Have an open mind about what might be causing the difficulty and be sensitive to the child's/young person's needs.

- Be mindful that, as foster carers or adoptive parents, you have a great deal of resources and experience that equip you to help the child/young person to manage the issue effectively.

- Be flexible in your approach and open to suggestions and creative ways of engaging with children and young people who are experiencing difficulties.

- Take the opportunity to be open about your feelings, including any difficulties with professionals who are available to help – although it won't resolve the issue immediately, feeling that you have been able to air your frustration helps to share the burden of responsibility for tackling the problem.

- Be prepared to change the way in which you approach the problem, if necessary.

Don't:

- Make assumptions about the cause of the issue.

- Be tempted to have a knee-jerk reaction to the issue – many difficulties are resolved in a relatively short period of time with a great deal of patience and sensitivity.

- Ignore the issue – although some foster carers have reported that they have been advised to ignore wetting and soiling issues, it is important that you do not do this, from a hygiene point of view. It is not an issue that will go away on its own.

- Have negative or indiscriminate discussions in the presence of the child.

- Allow the problem to become the focus of family life.

PARENTING CHILDREN AFFECTED BY TOILETING ISSUES

Case studies

Based on my experience of working with a wide range
of families and professional networks, in this section
of the book I present a selection of anonymised,
unidentifiable case studies to highlight some of the issues
that have arisen for children, young people and their
families, and ways in which they have been addressed.

Annie

Annie was 14 years old and lived with her siblings in a
long-term foster care placement. Overall, she seemed
happy at home and at school. She had a wide circle of
friends and participated in various sporting activities.
Her foster carers were concerned because Annie started
to wet the bed six months ago. Her foster mother also
reported that Annie sometimes had wet or damp pants
when she came home from school, and she had noticed
an unpleasant odour. Although Annie had seen her GP
and attended an enuresis clinic, she did not like talking to
anybody about it. She had started to conceal the wetting
episodes and did not mention them to anyone. A medical
assessment concluded that there were no physical health
issues to be concerned about, related to the wetting
episodes.

In addition, Annie's foster carers were not happy with

the contact arrangements in place between Annie and her birth family. They thought that the wetting episodes could be linked to stress as a result of contact. Annie did not want to see the school nurse or to attend the enuresis clinic again.

The foster carers approached Annie's social worker, who asked the LAC nurse for advice. The LAC nurse was aware that Annie might not want to speak directly about the issue and so arranged a home visit to undertake routine health reviews regarding Annie and her siblings. Prior to the visit, the LAC nurse had a discreet discussion with the foster carer about Annie's wetting problem. As is usual practice, the LAC nurse then met with each child individually for their health review.

In her review, Annie was chatty but she did not volunteer any information about the wetting problem. However, just as the LAC nurse was about to close the session, Annie started to talk about night times and not being able to sleep very well. The family dinner was ready, so the LAC nurse asked if she could visit Annie again the following week to talk more about getting to sleep, and Annie agreed.

The following week, Annie was less guarded and seemed open to discussing more personal matters. After meeting with the LAC nurse a few more times at home, several issues emerged. Annie confided that she woke early in the morning needing to go to the toilet but was worried about disturbing the household and had consequently wet the bed on several occasions. At school, it transpired, Annie was always in a rush – she was too busy with friends and did not always take enough time in the toilet to fully empty her bladder, which sometimes

65

led to her having wet pants in the day.

After several more visits, Annie agreed to talk with her foster carer and the LAC nurse together to try and find a way to manage the problem. They decided that it would not be helpful for Annie to have such a sensitive issue discussed at her LAC review.

They agreed that the bedroom arrangements could be slightly altered so that Annie could slip out to the toilet more easily. Annie's experience of sharing her worries with the LAC nurse at her own pace and being helped to find a workable solution, without feeling blamed or humiliated, gave her the confidence to share other things that were on her mind.

She started to indicate that there was more that she wanted to talk about, and the LAC nurse asked Annie if she would like to see the LAC CAMHS worker, which she agreed to do. Annie found it hard to attend CAMHS at first; she had developed a trusting relationship with the LAC nurse and found it difficult to meet with another professional, and cancelled several appointments. However, encouraged by her foster carer and the LAC nurse, Annie started to attend regular sessions at CAMHS. She had many worries and questions about what had happened in her past and uncertainty about what was going to happen in the future, which she was able to talk with her CAMHS worker about.

Discussion points

Annie's experience highlights the importance of not jumping to conclusions or making assumptions about what might be causing the difficulty. Annie's situation was quite complex; although her wetting episodes had initially brought her problems to her foster carers' attention, they had thought that the issue was related to anxiety about Annie's contact with her birth parents. However, over time, it transpired that this was not the case.

Although Annie's wetting also appeared to be linked to her not spending enough time in the toilet, a problem which was quickly and easily resolved, as time went on it became apparent that she had underlying emotional issues with which she needed help. To begin with, Annie's foster carer was convinced that Annie's difficulties had a physical base and understandably became frustrated and requested practical solutions. However, she was flexible and open to receiving support, and although Annie had a history of not wanting to engage with professionals, she was able to work together with the LAC nurse to facilitate Annie's engagement with her and then later with the LAC worker at CAMHS.

The way in which foster carers, adoptive parents and professionals engage with young people is crucial. It took quite a long time for Annie to feel safe enough to let the LAC nurse know about some of her anxieties about the future. The pace of the meetings was led by Annie, who only slowly became confident enough to share her concerns. This led to her being referred to CAMHS, where she was able to explore her underlying emotional difficulties in more depth.

Neil

Neil, aged 12, was removed from his parents' care at the age of seven, due to a chronic history of neglect. He lived with his grandparents for several years before being placed in foster care when they were no longer able to meet his needs. His social worker reported that Neil had a very poor diet when he lived with his grandparents. He did not eat much fresh fruit or vegetables and he regularly suffered with constipation to the point of needing to take medication to help him to have a poo. Whilst living with his grandparents, Neil had had to care for himself a lot of the time. His morning routine was very rushed, and he often did not have time to have breakfast or to use the toilet before leaving for school. His grandparents reported that they thought Neil had a significant medical bowel problem.

Neil's teachers contacted his foster carers to let them

know that he often arrived at school with poo in his pants after getting off the school bus. The foster carers told Neil's social worker about the problem and requested help to manage it. The foster carer did not think that Neil would want to talk with the social worker; she thought that he might feel too embarrassed and was surprised when he agreed to meet with her. Neil told his social worker how much he missed his grandparents and their dogs.

The social worker contacted the school nurse who arranged a meeting with the foster carers. Together they used ERIC resources (see Useful Resources) to help Neil to develop a common language to explore and understand his pooing difficulties. Neil did not seem to be at all worried or self-conscious about his soiling accidents and was happy to talk about going to the toilet and his difficulties pooing. He had a warm relationship with his foster mother, and she came to understand that Neil had not had any help with toilet training or how to recognise his own body signals when he was an infant and was therefore unable to link the bodily sensation of needing a poo with going to the toilet. Together they agreed that they would try and recognise Neil's signals for needing the toilet, but that he would also take a spare set of clothes to school to change into when he arrived, if necessary. After a few months the soiling incidents reduced significantly, and Neil developed confidence in understanding when his body told him that he needed to use the toilet.

Discussion points

Neil's problem with poo in his pants was relatively quickly and easily resolved. In his case, the issue was related to earlier parenting, when he had not been sufficiently helped to develop an awareness of his body's signals. By this, I mean the kind of situation when a small child might fidget uncomfortably or shift from one foot to another, and a parent would suggest that they might need to go for a poo. Neil's problem was exacerbated by a long history of constipation due to a lack of fresh fruit and fibre in his diet.

Due to his age, Neil's foster carers and social worker had assumed that he had been toilet trained and was able to attend to his personal hygiene independently. With patience and by developing a shared understanding of the problem, Neil's foster carers were able to take a few developmental steps backwards in the way they related to him, by helping him to recognise his body's signals for needing a poo, and reminding him to go to the toilet, which enabled him to catch up developmentally. The problem was resolved within a few months.

Nahim

Nahim, aged five, had been removed from his birth
mother when he was two years old due to concerns
about neglect. His mother had mental health difficulties
and was in a violent relationship with her new partner,
having separated from Nahim's father during the
pregnancy. She was very preoccupied with her own
difficulties and Nahim and his siblings were often left
alone with little or no food. The family home was dirty
and unkempt. Nahim was the youngest child and had
mainly been cared for by his older birth siblings, who
took responsibility for feeding him. All the children were
removed from home and placed in foster care. Nahim
was separated from his siblings and returned to his
mother's care several times before the decision was made
to remove him permanently from his birth family. Nahim's
older siblings were placed in long-term foster care and he
was placed in a short-term foster home as it was hoped

SECTION II

71

that an adoptive family would be found for him.

After spending two years in several different short-term foster placements, Nahim was adopted when he was five years old by a young couple who had an older birth son. Nahim appeared to settle into his adoptive family very quickly, but after a few months his behaviour started to deteriorate. He became very clingy to his adoptive mother and angry when she showed affection to her older son, which the family found difficult to manage. He was also reported to steal food from home and from other children at school, despite having an adequate packed lunch every day that he did not finish.

Bedwetting had been a problem for Nahim since moving to his adoptive family. Nahim's adoptive mother had made a reward chart with him, which had proved to be partially successful, but she was concerned that the wetting remained an issue.

Nahim's adoptive parents had agreed to an "open" adoption so that he could maintain contact with his birth siblings, with whom he had a close bond. However, they noticed that his wetting increased around the time of scheduled meetings, and they wondered whether they should stop Nahim's contact with his siblings.

Nahim's adoptive mother sought advice from their GP. The GP referred Nahim to his local CAMHS because Nahim was also experiencing difficulties with his behaviour at home and at school, and was not making friends.

CAMHS staff met with Nahim's adoptive parents, who described his background of chronic neglect. The social

worker had told them that Nahim was often left in
the dark for long periods at home and had been too
frightened to get up and go to the toilet in the night, so
they had bought him a night light and encouraged him to
wake them if he was frightened or needed help, but he
never did.

Nahim's adoptive parents described how he found the
slightest change difficult to manage and that it would
lead to an increase in wetting incidents. It took him a
long time to settle into his new school and he became
very unsettled again at the start of each new term. He
seemed unable to allow himself to enjoy or find pleasure
in things that other children of his age looked forward
to. For example, a much anticipated family holiday caused
him huge anxiety; he persistently questioned his adoptive
parents about the timings, where they were going to
stay and when they would return home. He also worked
himself up into a heightened state of anxiety before
school trips and then had wetting accidents, which made
him feel embarrassed and ashamed.

The family met with a family therapist initially, and after
a period of seeing the family together and spending time
talking and thinking about how they were all getting used
to being a family, it was thought that it might be helpful
for Nahim to have some sessions on his own with a child
and adolescent psychotherapist.

In his individual sessions, Nahim spent time drawing
pictures and telling stories about living in a dark cave
with no food, and as he got more in touch with his
earlier experiences, he became very anxious and rushed
to the toilet to have a wee or poo. Alongside Nahim's
sessions, his adoptive parents continued to meet with

the family therapist, who helped them to understand some of the meaning of Nahim's behaviour, and how to respond to it in a way that helped him to feel safe. For example, it was important for Nahim to have a predictable routine and to talk to him about school trips and holidays well in advance, so that he could gradually get used to the idea of change, and be supported to regulate his feelings.

Nahim's adoptive mother reported that, very slowly, wetting incidents reduced, although they presented again at holiday times and on occasions when he found it difficult to regulate his feelings.

Discussion points

This case highlights some of the complex issues that adopted children and their adoptive families and siblings encounter. Due to his early experience of neglect, Nahim had not known an adult who was consistently available to meet his needs, and he felt that he had to rely on his own resources: stealing food and not calling for help in the night when he needed the toilet – because previously there had been no response, he had become accustomed to not asking. Nahim had also moved many times in his short life. He had stayed with some foster carers who were warm and had been able to meet his needs, but given the short-term nature of the placements, he had no opportunity to form close attachments. Therefore, when he was adopted, he could not quite trust that he was not going to move again. It took a long time, nearly three years, before Nahim fully settled into his adoptive family. He became more integrated at school, formed a solid friendship group, and the wetting incidents gradually stopped.

Suzie

Suzie, aged nine, had been living in her foster care placement for three years and had started soiling a year ago. Suzie's birth mother had died six months previously. Her foster carer was concerned because her soiling was becoming more frequent and had started to happen whilst they were out in public as well as at home. The family was a busy one, with other foster children moving in and out as Suzie's foster carer also offered short-term placements. In particular, two other children had moved in 18 months previously, originally for a two week stay, but they were still with the family. Suzie only seemed to have "accidents" when she was with her foster mother – not when she was with her foster father.

Suzie's foster mother shared her concerns with the LAC nurse, who spoke with Suzie, but she was reluctant to talk about the difficulty and appeared ashamed of it.

It became apparent that this had become an extremely frustrating and distressing issue for Suzie's foster mother, who was struggling to manage a number of children of different ages with varying degrees of need due to their difficult early life histories and circumstances.

Suzie's social worker and the LAC nurse wondered whether Suzie might feel a bit "lost" at times in this big, busy family and whether she would benefit from more individual attention. They shared their thoughts with Suzie's foster mother, who was initially sceptical about the suggestion that she might be part of the solution, as she felt that she had already tried everything and was pressing for counselling for Suzie, as the situation had reached crisis point.

However, Suzie's foster mother agreed to set aside a little more time to do something individually with Suzie, who looked forward to the time they spent together. Things improved slightly, although the situation was not totally resolved. Some weeks later, when the LAC nurse visited her at home, Suzie told her that she had a poo accident when she saw something that frightened her on the computer. Suzie's foster mother also noticed that if she appeared to be angry with Suzie, it would often result in soiled pants. She admitted that she had initially thought that soiling was a way for Suzie to seek attention from her, or a means of retaliation because she was being "told off". The LAC nurse encouraged the foster carer to keep a diary of Suzie's pooing accidents and it became apparent that they were related to situations when Suzie was in an acute state of anxiety. Suzie's social worker shared information about Suzie's exposure to domestic violence between her mother and step-father whilst living in her birth family. Suzie had often been frightened and had hidden and soiled herself on numerous occasions, and they wondered whether Suzie's pooing accident after having been on the computer had been triggered by a memory related to something she had seen online.

Discussion points

This case highlights the tension placed on the relationship between a child and foster carer/adoptive parent when the issue becomes extremely difficult to manage and the placement is almost at breaking point. The foster mother was extremely angry with Suzie for what she considered to be "attention-seeking" behaviour. The stress that the difficulty caused her led to her becoming inflexible and quite punitive in her response to Suzie, which only served to exacerbate Suzie's anxiety and led to more frequent soiling as she evacuated her anxiety in a very concrete way. But in spite of the difficulties, the foster mother had a good enough relationship with the social worker and LAC nurse to enable her to be open about her anger and frustration, which helped to contain the situation. By working together, they were able to identify that the pooing accidents were Suzie's body's way of responding to stress and anxiety, as well as a possible reaction to the grief of losing her mother.

James

James was a four-year-old boy who had lived with his mother and teenage sisters before being taken into care. James's mother was a single parent who had also spent periods of her childhood in local authority care. His home environment was chaotic. His sisters had issues with drug addiction, and his mother had mental health difficulties and had not been able to set appropriate boundaries, which led to the family home becoming a base for gang activities and drug dealing. James's mother had relied on him as a source of comfort, wanting to keep him close to her in a baby-like state, and so, at the point when he was removed into foster care, he had not reached his developmental milestones or been potty trained.

James was initially placed in a short-term foster placement, as it was hoped that an adoptive family would be found for him. At first, he exhibited many behavioural difficulties and would purposefully break all of the toys in his room. James's foster mother was extremely patient and after six months, James's behaviour started to settle down. Sadly, his foster mother suddenly became very physically unwell and was unexpectedly admitted to hospital for a long period of time. At that point, James was moved to a different foster placement. His new foster carer reported that James had started frequently wetting, soiling and smearing. She was finding his behaviour very difficult to manage, along with the practical burden of the additional laundry that it produced. She asked the social worker for help because she felt that the placement was at breaking point.

James was referred to his local CAMHS for support. CAMHS staff met with his foster carer and social worker to explore the difficulties. The social worker was able to give a good account of James's early history. It was clear that he had experienced a lot of disrupted attachments in a relatively brief period during his short life, as a result of his separation from his mother and birth siblings, followed by the abrupt disappearance from his life of his foster mother, who had become a trusted and reliable parental figure for him.

The CAMHS workers thought that it would be helpful for James's foster carer to have sessions on her own, in order to give her support and the opportunity to talk about the issues, before having further sessions together with James. During her sessions with the CAMHS therapist, they considered the impact on James of the sudden separation from his previous foster carer and how, given his age and developmental delay, he did not have the language to express his worries, which appeared to be concretely spilling out of him and which he angrily smeared on the walls at home. They agreed that it would not be helpful for the foster carer to be punitive in her response and that it would be necessary to go back to basics in terms of supporting James with toilet training. The foster carer used a reward chart to record when James managed to use the toilet independently. He responded well and looked forward to choosing his favourite stickers to put on the chart. She also arranged to have some special time with James before he went to sleep and encouraged him to choose a bedtime story. When it felt appropriate, she took him to visit his previous foster carer to say a proper goodbye. When the therapists met with James and his foster carer, through observing and commenting on his play, they were able to start to think together about angry, messy feelings that he had inside and needed to get rid of.

Discussion points

This case study highlights the impact on James of the traumatic separations, first from his birth family and then his foster carer, followed by a transition to a new placement. James's second foster carer was initially sceptical about having the resources to help manage his difficulties. However, she persevered with the CAMHS sessions and reflected later that it was her growing understanding about how James lacked the emotional language to express his fear and anxiety about his experiences, and her realisation that he was communicating his difficulties through his actions, that helped her to become more open to the idea that his behaviour was not deliberately provocative. His behaviour remained difficult to manage, but the pooing and smearing incidents reduced considerably after James settled into a routine, and a period of stability was reached.

Lucy

Lucy, aged 10, was adopted when she was six years old. Her birth mother was very vulnerable and misused drugs. She had given birth to Lucy when she was 17, and Lucy had been removed from her care when she was four years old due to neglect and physical abuse, as well as concerns that she may have been sexually abused by her mother's then current partner. She lived in foster care before moving to her adoptive home. As a result of her earlier experiences, Lucy was developmentally delayed and presented as younger than her chronological age. She took a long time to settle with her adoptive parents, who noted that she was a very anxious, secretive little girl who found even the slightest change difficult to manage, and she often resisted help. Although Lucy's foster carers had helped her to become toilet trained before she moved to her adoptive family, she continued to have wetting accidents and occasionally smeared poo in the bathroom.

Lucy's adoptive parents took her to their GP because they felt concerned that, aged 10, she still had wetting accidents during the day and also regularly wet the bed. They found that they had to encourage her to use the toilet during the day when they noticed her jigging about uncomfortably, as she did not seem to register when she needed to wee. School staff also reported that Lucy was having wetting accidents, and was sometimes teased by other children.

Lucy's adoptive mother was extremely patient and had initially approached the issue very sensitively with her. She talked to her about having noticed the bed being wet in the morning and asked her what was the matter. Lucy became very angry and strongly denied the wetting incidents, despite the evidence of the wet bedding. She also regularly concealed wet items of clothing about the house, which frustrated her adoptive parents, as they found it very difficult to get rid of the smell of stale urine in the wash, and regularly had to throw items of clothing away. This added to their sense of frustration, and the arguments became quite heated, which sometimes resulted in a smearing incident, further adding to the conflict.

The GP referred Lucy to an enuresis clinic and various strategies were tried. The continence nurse was satisfied that there was not an underlying medical cause and she worked together with Lucy's adoptive mother to try new strategies, which they also shared with school staff. Lucy's mother ensured that the school had a fresh supply of clothing in case Lucy had a wetting accident. At home, she used an incontinence sheet on Lucy's bed.

She encouraged Lucy to choose a laundry basket for her room in which she could put the wet bedding and clothes. This went some way towards containing the issue, but Lucy occasionally still wet the bed.

Lucy and her adoptive family were referred to a specialist fostering and adoption team based in CAMHS. They met with workers who had a lot of experience of supporting families with similar issues. Lucy's adoptive parents began to understand that she was smearing as a means of communicating her anger and frustration, rather than being deliberately aggressive towards them, which helped them to moderate their responses, and after some considerable time and a lot of patience, the situation calmed down considerably. Although the incidents of smearing stopped, Lucy still sometimes wet the bed, but with help from her adoptive mother, she gradually learned to manage this independently.

Discussion points

This case highlights how difficult it is for adoptive parents to tackle the issue when the child or young person flatly denies that there is a problem, despite evidence to the contrary, and how the problem can become quite entrenched. Lucy denied that there was a problem and was unable to provide a reason for her actions. Children who have been abused at a very young age do not have the language to communicate their experiences or their feelings verbally, and smearing can sometimes be a way of communicating their anger and distress. On the continence nurse's advice, Lucy's adoptive mother left some clean bedding and nightclothes out for her and asked her to change everything if she had a wet bed, which she reluctantly agreed to do. It transpired that she had been chastised

83

for having wetting accidents when she was in her birth mother's care, and therefore denied that she wet the bed for fear of physical punishment, which had been her previous experience.

References

Anon (1987) 'My enuresis', *Archives of Disease in Childhood*, 62, pp866–868

Bion W (1962) *Learning from Experience*, London: Heinemann

Bowlby J (1951) *Maternal Care and Mental Health*, World Health Organization Monograph (Serial No. 2), Geneva: World Health Organization

Buckner JD, Lopez C, Dunkel S and Joiner Jr TE (2008) 'Behaviour management training for the treatment of reactive attachment disorder', *Child Maltreatment*, 13, pp289–297

Butler RJ (1987) *Nocturnal Enuresis: Psychological perspectives*, Bristol: John Wright & Son

Butler RJ (1994) *Nocturnal Enuresis:The child's experience*, Oxford: Butterworth Heinemann

Department for Education (2015) *Working Together to Safeguard Children:A guide to inter-agency working to safeguard and promote the welfare of children*, London: DfE

Department for Education (2018) *Children Looked After in England including Adoption: 2017 to 2018*, London: DfE

Ford T,Vostanis P, Meltzer H and Goodman R (2007) 'Psychiatric disorder among British children looked after by local authorities: comparison with children living in private households', *British Journal of Psychiatry*, 190, pp319–325

Gould J (2011) 'Nocturnal enuresis and constipation in children and young people', *Adoption & Fostering*, 35:1, pp90–93

Jarvelin MR, Moilanen I,Vikevainen-Tervonen L and Huttunen HP (1990) 'Life changes and protective capacities in enuretic and non-enuretic children', *Journal of Child Psychology and Psychiatry,* 31, pp763–774

Joinson C (2018) 'Not life threatening but life ruining: continence problems in young people', paper presented by Dr Carol Joinson, Centre for Child & Adolescent Health, University of Bristol, at Association for Young People's Health – 10th Anniversary Conference, 21 February, Institute of Child Health, London

Kalo BB and Bella H (1996) 'Enuresis: prevalence and associated factors among primary school children in Saudi Arabia', *Acta Paediatrica*, 85, pp1217–1222

Meltzer H, Corbin T, Gatwood R, Goodman R and Ford T (2003) *The Mental Health of Young People Looked After by Local Authorities in*

England, London: HMSO

Mosca N and Schatz M (2013) 'Encopresis: not just an accident', *NASN School Nurse*, 28:5, pp218–221

NICE (2010a) *Nocturnal Enuresis: The management of bedwetting in children and young people*, Clinical Guideline 111, available at: www. guidance.nice.org.uk

NICE (2010b) *Constipation in Children and Young People: Diagnosis and management*, updated 2017, Clinical Guideline 99, available at: www. guidance.nice.org.uk

Rutter M, Kreppner J and Sonuga-Barke E (2009) 'Emanuel Miller Lecture: Attachment insecurity, disinhibited attachment, and attachment disorders: where do research findings leave the concepts?' *Journal of Child Psychology & Psychiatry & Allied Disciplines*, 50, pp529–543

Schore AN (2001) 'The effects of early relational trauma on right brain development, affect regulation, and infant mental health', *Infant Mental Health Journal,* 22, pp201–269

Sempik J, Ward H and Darker I (2008) 'Emotional and behavioural difficulties of children and young people at entry into care', *Clinical Child Psychology & Psychiatry*, 13:2, pp221–233

Von Gontard A, Hollman E, Elberg H, Benden B, Rittig S and Lehmkuhl G (1997) 'Clinical enuresis phenotypes in familial nocturnal enuresis', *Scandinavian Journal of Urology and Nephrology*, 31: 183, pp11–16

Weaver A, Dobson P and Swithinbank L (2004) 'Addressing the needs of teenagers with continence problems', *The Nursing Times*, 100:20, p61

Williams J, Jackson S, Maddocks A, Cheung W-Y, Love A and Hutchings H (2001) 'Case-control study of the health of those looked after by local authorities', *Archives of Disease in Childhood*, 85, pp280–285

Woolgar M and Baldock E (2015) 'Attachment disorders versus more common problems in looked after and adopted children: comparing community and expert assessments', *Child & Adolescent Mental Health*, 20, pp34–40

Zeanah CH, Berlin LJ and Boris NW (2011) 'Practitioner review: clinical applications of attachment theory and research for infants and young children', *Journal of Child Psychology & Psychiatry*, 52, pp819–833

Reading resources for children

Whelan Banks J (2008) *Liam Goes Poo in the Toilet: A story about trouble with toilet training*, London: Jessica Kingsley Publishers

Gomi T (2004) *Everybody Poos*, London: Frances Lincoln Children's Books

Glossary

ADHD – Attention Deficit Hyperactivity Disorder.

Aetiology – The cause, set of causes, or manner of causation of a disease or condition.

Anticholinergics – a broad class of drug used to treat a variety of medical conditions that affect the contraction and relaxation of muscles.

Attachment – an emotional bond between an infant or toddler and their primary caregiver.

Autism (Autism spectrum disorder, ASD) – the name for a range of similar conditions, including Asperger syndrome, that affect a person's social interaction, communication, interests and behaviour.

Bladder epispadias – condition where the urethra does not form properly.

Bladder exstrophy – a congenital abnormality that occurs when the skin over the lower abdominal wall (bottom part of the tummy) does not form properly. "Extrophy" means turned inside out. Therefore the bladder is open and exposed on the outside of the abdomen.

CAMHS – Child and Adolescent Mental Health Services.

Cerebral palsy – the name for a group of lifelong conditions that affect movement and co-ordination, caused by a problem with the brain that occurs before, during or soon after birth.

Comorbidity – the occurrence of one or more disorders in the same person at the same time or in some causal sequence.

Conduct disorders – a range of antisocial types of behaviour displayed in childhood or adolescence.

Continence – bowel and bladder control.

Continence nurse – a clinical nurse specialist who assesses and supports adults and children who have bladder or bowel problems.

Cortisol – a steroid hormone that is produced by the adrenal glands. When released into the bloodstream, cortisol can act on many different parts of the body and can help the body respond to stress or danger.

Cystometry – a test used to look for problems with the filling and emptying of the bladder which helps to diagnose urine control problems.

Desmopressin – a man-made form of a hormone that occurs naturally in the pituitary gland and is used to treat bedwetting.

Down's syndrome – a genetic condition that typically includes some level of learning disability and characteristic physical features.

Encopresis – the soiling of underwear by children who are past the age of toilet training. It occurs when a child dirties his pants or poos in inappropriate places, for example, on his bed, or in rooms other than the toilet.

Enuresis – a term used for wetting or passing of urine without control at an age when control would be expected. This can occur either during the day (diurnal enuresis) or night (nocturnal enuresis).

Faecal impaction – faecal impaction of the colon occurs when stool becomes stuck in the colon and cannot leave the body.

Idiopathic constipation – when the exact cause of constipation is unknown.

Intra-uterine – within the uterus.

Laxative – a drug or medicine that facilitates evacuation of the bowels.

Learning disabilities – these affect the way in which a person learns new things throughout their lifetime.

Multidisciplinary – combining or involving several academic disciplines or professional specialisations in an approach to a topic or problem.

Neurodevelopmental disorders – disabilities in the functioning of the brain that affect a child's behaviour, memory or ability to learn.

Neuropsychological – looks at how the health of the brain affects thinking skills and behaviour.

Neuroscience – the study of how the nervous system develops, its structure, and what it does.

NICE – National Institute for Clinical Excellence.

Oxybutynin – a medication used to treat certain bladder and urinary conditions (e.g. overactive bladder). It relaxes the muscles in the bladder to help decrease problems of urgency and frequent urination.

Paediatrician – a medical doctor who manages the physical, behavioural and mental care of children from birth until age 18.

Physiological – the branch of biology relating to the function of organs and organ systems, and how they work within the body to respond to challenges.

Primary bedwetting – bedwetting that has been ongoing since early childhood without a break. A child with primary bedwetting has never been dry at night for any significant length of time.

Primary encopresis – children who have had continuous soiling problems throughout their life.

Protective factors – conditions or attributes in individuals, families, communities, or the larger society that, when present, mitigate or eliminate risk in families and communities and that increase the health and well-being of children and families.

Psyche – the mind, or the deepest thoughts, feelings or beliefs of a person or group.

Psychoanalytic – relating to psychoanalysis.

PTSD (Post-Traumatic Stress Disorder) – an anxiety disorder caused by very stressful, frightening or distressing events.

Scatolia – refers to playing with and/or the smearing of poo.

Secondary bedwetting – bedwetting that starts after the child has been dry at night for a significant period of time, at least six months.

Secondary encopresis – soiling that starts after the child has been toilet trained – often prompted by a stressful experience, such as starting school, or because of underlying chronic constipation.

Trycyclics – any of a group of pharmacologically active substances that share a common three-ring structure.

Urinary tract infection (UTI) – common infections that can affect the bladder, kidneys and the tubes connected to them.

Urodynamic tests – any procedure that looks at how well the bladder, sphincters and urethra are storing and releasing urine.

Vasopressin – a naturally occurring hormone that helps control various bodily functions.

Useful organisations

Mumsnet

www.mumsnet.com

A popular website for parents which pools knowledge and experience from its contributors on a range of child-related subjects.

Netmums

www.netmums.com

A popular parenting website that acts as a local network of sites, providing knowledge and experience from local contributors.

Adoption, Fostering and Kinship Care Service

Children, Young Adults and Families Department
Tavistock and Portman NHS Foundation Trust
120 Belsize Lane
London NW3 5BA
Tel: 020 7435 7111
https://tavistockandportman.nhs.uk/care-and-treatment/our-clinical-services/adoption-fostering-and-kinship-care/
An NHS service that provides services for looked after and adopted children and their families, where children are experiencing emotional or behavioural difficulties.

Anna Freud National Centre for Children and Families

12 Maresfield Gardens
London NW3 5SU
Tel: 020 7794 2313
www.annafreud.org/
A children's mental health charity that supports children and their families with mental health difficulties.

Bladder and Bowel UK

Burrows House
10 Priestley Road
Wardley Industrial Estate
Worsley M28 2LY
Tel: 0161 607 8219
www.bbuk.org.uk/
A charity that provides information and advice on bowel and bladder issues in children and adults to the public and professionals.

Caspari Foundation

Finspace
225–229 Seven Sisters Road
London N4 2DA
Helpline: 0808 169 9949
www.caspari.org.uk/
A charity that helps children and young people overcome emotional, learning and behavioural difficulties. Provides educational psychotherapy to children in some areas of London, along with training for school staff.

ERIC (Education and Resources for Improving Childhood Continence)

36 Old School House
Kingswood
Bristol BS15 8DB

Helpline: 0808 169 9949
www.eric.org.uk/
A charity that provides support and advice for families of children and young people with bowel and bladder difficulties.

Family Action

24 Angel Gate
City Road
London EC1V 2PT
Tel: 020 7254 6251
www.family-action.org.uk/
A charity providing practical, emotional and financial support to families who are experiencing poverty, disadvantage and social isolation.

Family Futures

3 and 4 Floral Place
7–9 Northhampton Grove
London N1 2PL
Tel: 020 7354 4161
www.familyfutures.co.uk/
An independent adoption support and adoption agency that specialises in providing therapy services for children who are traumatised or who have attachment difficulties, as well as support to adopters and carers.

Fostering Network

87 Blackfriars Road
London SE1 8HA
Tel: 020 7620 6400
www.thefosteringnetwork.org.uk/
A charity that provides information, advice and support to everyone who is involved in the lives of fostered children.

National Children's Bureau

WeWork

115 Mare Street

London E8 4RU

Tel: 020 7843 6000

www.ncb.org.uk/

A charity that provides information, advice and resources to help improve the lives of disadvantaged children, particularly those who are disabled or particularly vulnerable.

PAC-UK (Post-Adoption Centre)

5 Torriano Mews

Torriano Avenue

London NW5 2RZ

Tel: 020 7284 0555

www.pac-uk.org/

A charity that provides specialist therapy, advice, support, counselling and training for all those affected by adoption and permanency.

Young Minds

Baden Place

London SE1 1YW

Parent helpline: 0808 802 5544

www.youngminds.org

A children's mental health charity that provides information, advice and support for children, professionals, parents and carers.